Why Math Maze

M000317658

Research has shown that repetition is essential for the brain to learn and recall information. Furthermore, children have a tendency to repeat activities they enjoy. The engaging mazes and other activities in this book will provide your child with repeated practice of grade-level-appropriate math skills. Continued practice with these skills helps develop a strong understanding of basic math concepts and builds a solid foundation in math problem solving, an important tool for academic success.

Upon your child's completion of each activity, use the provided incentive chart and stickers to track progress and celebrate your child's success.

SKILLS

- Numbers through 100
- Counting by 2s, 5s, and 10s
- Addition
- Subtraction
- Patterns
- Place value
- Money
- Multistep problem solving

HOW YOU CAN HELP SUPPORT LEARNING

- Encourage your child to use manipulatives, such as paper clips, beans, coins, and counting blocks, to model problems and connect meaning to the written words and symbols.
- Have your child draw pictures to represent the data or draw a number line to assist with addition and subtraction problems.
- Assist your child in identifying key math terms, such as *in all*, *altogether*, *sum*, *take away*, *from*, *difference*, *even*, *odd*, *equal*, *greater than*, and *less than*. Ask your child to explain his or her answers.
- Give hints rather than solutions to particularly tricky problems.
- Have your child check answers to addition and subtraction problems by working backward.

The Beehive Maze

Circle the **odd** numbers to help the bee get to the hive.

Friendship Bracelets

Start with **8**. Subtract the numbers between Mia and each friend. Write the answer on each hat.

Find the Doghouse

Solve each addition problem. Then color all of the spaces
with sums of **10** to help the dog find the doghouse.

START

9 + 1 *10*	8 + 3 *11*	5 + 7 *19*	10 + 1 *9*
5 + 5 *10*	6 + 4 *10*	6 + 5 *11*	7 + 1 *8*
5 + 3 *8*	10 + 0 *10*	3 + 4 *7*	1 + 8 *9*
2 + 9 *11*	7 + 3 *10*	4 + 6 *10*	8 + 2 *10*
3 + 3 *6*	5 + 6 *15*	2 + 7 *9*	3 + 7 *10*

FINISH

Missing Numbers

Fill in the missing numbers. Then color all of the spaces with **odd** numbers to help the ants get ready for the picnic.

1	2	3	4	5
6	7	8	9	10
11	12	13	14	15
16	17	18	19	20
21	22	23	24	25
26	27	28	29	30

Something Fishy

Start with **13**. Subtract the numbers between the shark and each fish. Write the answer on each fish.

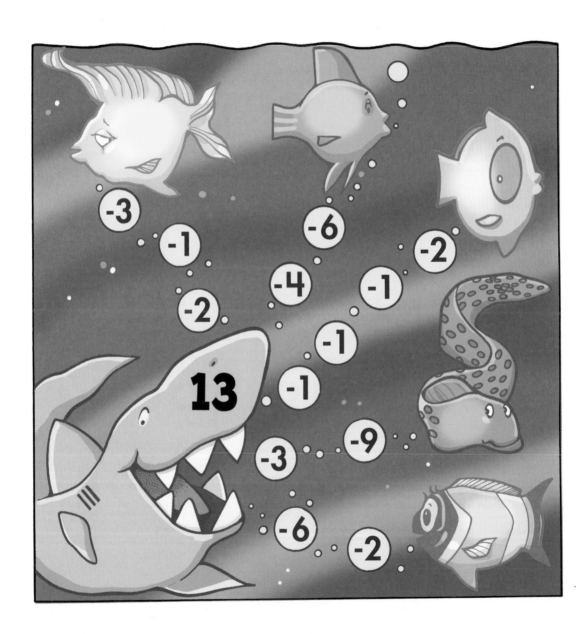

Lily Pad Path

Add. Color each lily pad that has a sum of **8** to find the frog's path.

1+7=____

0+8=____

6+3=____

4+4=____

5+3=____

2+6=____

7+1=____

3+5=____

6+1=____

8+0=____

6+2=____

The Prince and the Dragon

Draw a line on the path that goes from **25** to **50** to help the prince find his pet dragon.

A Worm's Treat

Add. Circle the sums that are **greater than 12** to help the worm find the watermelon.

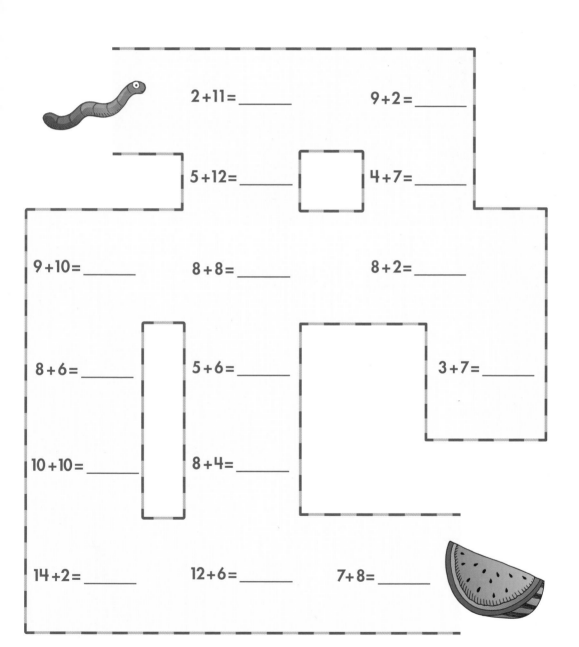

2+11=_____   9+2=_____

5+12=_____   4+7=_____

9+10=_____   8+8=_____   8+2=_____

8+6=_____   5+6=_____   3+7=_____

10+10=_____   8+4=_____

14+2=_____   12+6=_____   7+8=_____

Beth's Birthday Cake

Color the squares with **even** numbers to help Beth find her birthday cake.

START

2	14	17	23	11
9	8	12	15	29
3	13	26	35	31
21	5	10	27	7
25	19	22	4	6

FINISH

Silly Snake

Count by **5s** and fill in the missing numbers to get from the snake's head to its tail.

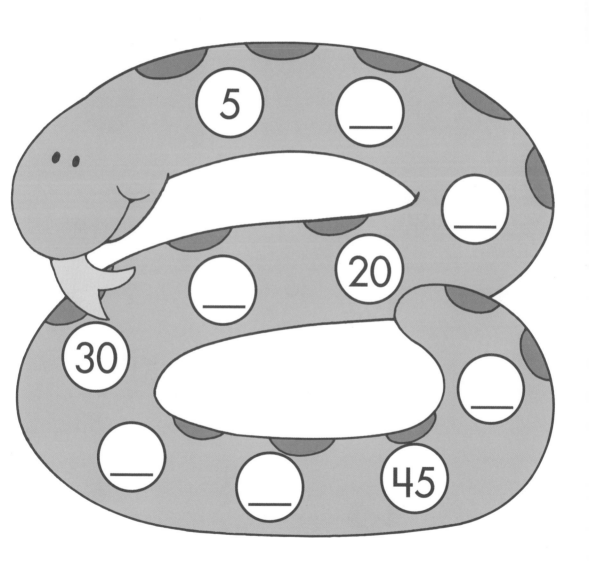

Busy Beaver

Start on **8**. Circle the numbers as you count by **2s** to help the beaver find the branch.

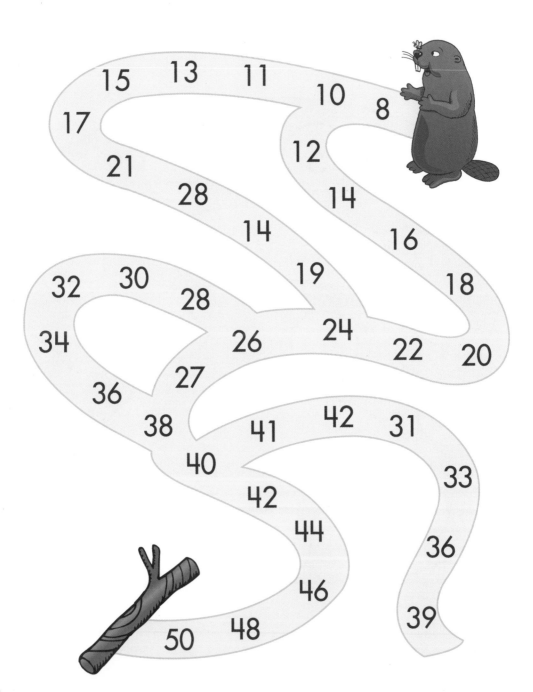

15 13 11
17   10 8
21   12
28   14
14   16
32 30   19 18
28
34   26 24 22 20
27
36
38 41 42 31
40 33
42
44 36
46 39
50 48

Monkey Math

Color the squares that have a **5** in the **ones place** to help the monkey find the banana.

START

5	150	54	56	50
55	15	105	25	550
51	500	151	35	53
59	57	58	75	52
65	45	85	95	154

FINISH

Watch Out for the Cat!

Count by **5**s and fill in the missing numbers to help the mice get to the cheese.

15   25   35   45   55   65   80   90

Farm Fun!

Draw a path to the farm from each arrow. Subtract the numbers along each path from **15**, and write your answers in the circles.

Counting by Twos

Count by **2**s and circle the numbers that lead to the playground.

1

2

3

12

4

5

8

6

10   11   12

7   8   9   13

1   14

16   15

17

18

school bus

Soap Box Derby

Circle the numbers that are **greater than 50** to help the mouse win the trophy.

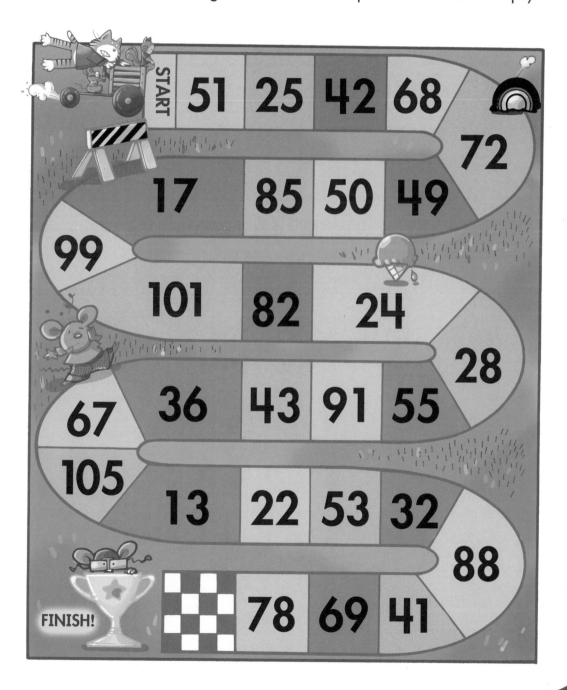

START

51 25 42 68

72

17 85 50 49

99

101 82 24

28

67 36 43 91 55

105

13 22 53 32

88

FINISH!

78 69 41

Camel Crossing

Subtract to find the answers. Then color answers in the sand to make a path for the camel.

1. 18
  − 3
  —

2. 14
  − 7
  —

3. 10
  − 7
  —

4. 17
  − 6
  —

5. 20
  − 11
  —

6. 16
  − 15
  —

7. 19
  − 14
  —

18   5
  7   4   10   14
23   3   13   33
  16   11   21   24
  2   9   6   19
  1   39   22   17
  15   12   25   8

Sums of 10

Circle each set of three numbers that adds up to **10**.

7	2	1	1	3
2	4	4	8	2
6	1	3	1	5

There are _____ sums of 10 altogether.

The Farmer's Veggies

Start with **10**. Subtract the numbers between the farmer and each veggie. Write the answers on the veggies.

The Magic Hat

Count by **2s** and circle the numbers from **36** to **70** to help the rabbit find the magic hat.

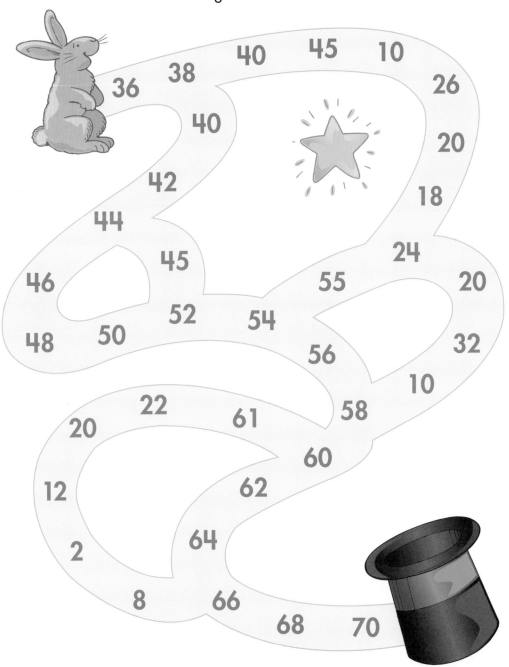

40 45 10
38 26
36
40 20
42 18
44
24
45 55 20
46
52 54
48 50 56 32
10
22 58
20 61
60
12 62
64
2
8 66
68 70

Sunflower Addition

Add the numbers along the path from the sun to the sunflower.

1 $2 + 7$ **2** $26 + 4$ **3** $14 + 5$ **4** $9 + 0$

5 $10 + 1$

9 $1 + 8$ **8** $7 + 5$ **7** $11 + 3$ **6** $3 + 2$

10 $3 + 9$ **11** $4 + 4$ **12** $12 + 3$ **13** $23 + 6$

14 $7 + 7$

18 $31 + 4$ **17** $5 + 6$ **16** $18 + 2$ **15** $9 + 8$

Number Bubbles

Follow the directions.

1 Start on 1 and count by **twos**. Fill in the missing numbers.

1   3   __   __   __   __   __   __   19

2 Start on 5 and count by **fives**. Fill in the missing numbers.

5   10   __   __   __   __   35   __   __   50

3 Start on 17 and count by **tens**. Fill in the missing numbers.

17   27   __   __   67   __   __   __   107

4 Start on 100 and count **backward by tens**. Fill in the missing numbers.

100   90   __   __   __   40   __   __   10

5 Start on 85 and count **backward by fives**. Fill in the missing numbers.

85   80   __   __   __   60   __   __   40

© 2012 CTP - 7218

Hop Home

Add. Circle the sums that are **less than 10** to help the frog hop home.

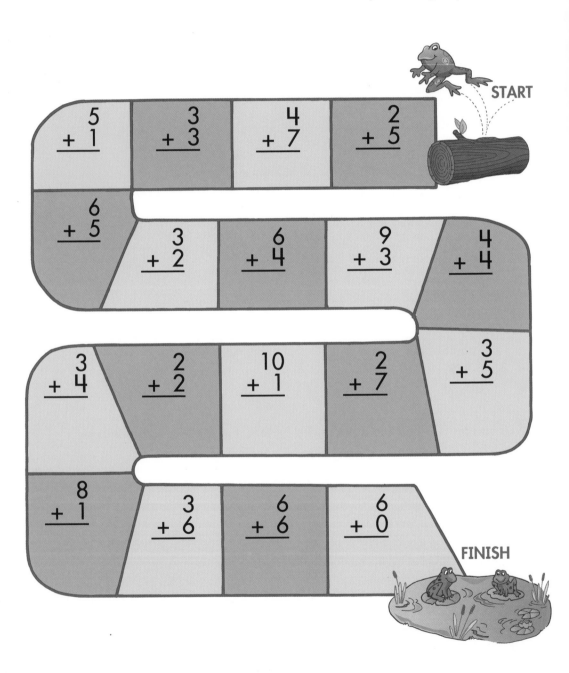

START

$\begin{array}{r} 5 \\ + 1 \\ \hline \end{array}$ $\begin{array}{r} 3 \\ + 3 \\ \hline \end{array}$ $\begin{array}{r} 4 \\ + 7 \\ \hline \end{array}$ $\begin{array}{r} 2 \\ + 5 \\ \hline \end{array}$

$\begin{array}{r} 6 \\ + 5 \\ \hline \end{array}$ $\begin{array}{r} 3 \\ + 2 \\ \hline \end{array}$ $\begin{array}{r} 6 \\ + 4 \\ \hline \end{array}$ $\begin{array}{r} 9 \\ + 3 \\ \hline \end{array}$ $\begin{array}{r} 4 \\ + 4 \\ \hline \end{array}$

$\begin{array}{r} 3 \\ + 4 \\ \hline \end{array}$ $\begin{array}{r} 2 \\ + 2 \\ \hline \end{array}$ $\begin{array}{r} 10 \\ + 1 \\ \hline \end{array}$ $\begin{array}{r} 2 \\ + 7 \\ \hline \end{array}$ $\begin{array}{r} 3 \\ + 5 \\ \hline \end{array}$

$\begin{array}{r} 8 \\ + 1 \\ \hline \end{array}$ $\begin{array}{r} 3 \\ + 6 \\ \hline \end{array}$ $\begin{array}{r} 6 \\ + 6 \\ \hline \end{array}$ $\begin{array}{r} 6 \\ + 0 \\ \hline \end{array}$

FINISH

Picnic Guest

Draw a path to the picnic basket from each arrow. Subtract the numbers along each path from **19**. Write your answers in the circles.

Find the Fact Families

Circle the fact families to follow the path and help the girl get home.

$9 + 4 = 13$
$4 + 9 = 13$

$11 + 3 = 14$
$7 + 7 = 14$

$5 + 7 = 12$
$7 + 5 = 12$

$6 + 3 = 9$
$7 + 2 = 9$

$8 + 6 = 14$
$6 + 8 = 14$

$12 + 4 = 16$
$10 + 6 = 16$

$5 + 5 = 10$
$7 + 3 = 10$

$9 + 9 = 18$
$10 + 8 = 18$

$4 + 5 = 9$
$8 + 1 = 9$

$12 + 8 = 20$
$8 + 12 = 20$

$9 + 2 = 11$
$5 + 6 = 11$

$3 + 4 = 7$
$4 + 3 = 7$

$13 + 6 = 19$
$6 + 13 = 19$

Subtraction Math Path

Start with **20** and subtract the numbers along the path to find the final answer.

Start	20	–		–	1	–
		2		4		2
		–		–		–
		5	–	0		3	= Finish

An Icy Path

Find the sums. Then color answers in the water to make a path for the penguin.

1. $2 + 2 = $ _____

2. $10 + 2 = $ _____

3. $22 + 2 = $ _____

4. $12 + 2 = $ _____

5. $36 + 2 = $ _____

6. $24 + 2 = $ _____

7. $18 + 2 = $ _____

5   1

9   7   4   21

27   11   31   12

39   43   24   69

47   25   14   47

26   38   65   63

20   51   73   77

00029647981

**Sell your books at
sellbackyourBook.com!**

Go to sellbackyourBook.com
and get an instant price quote.
We even pay the shipping - see
what your old books are worth
today!

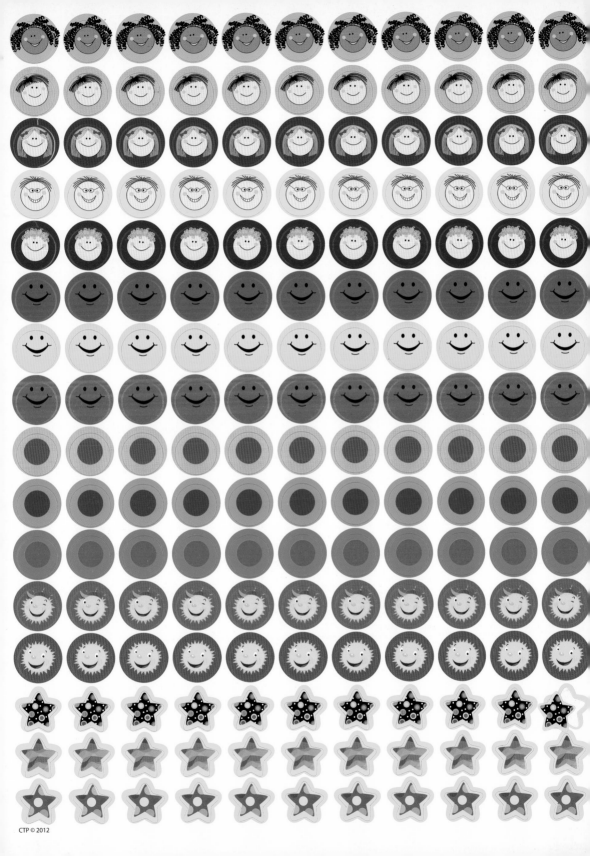

The Fairy's Magic Harp

Draw a line on the path that goes from **51** to **75** to help the fairy find the magic harp.

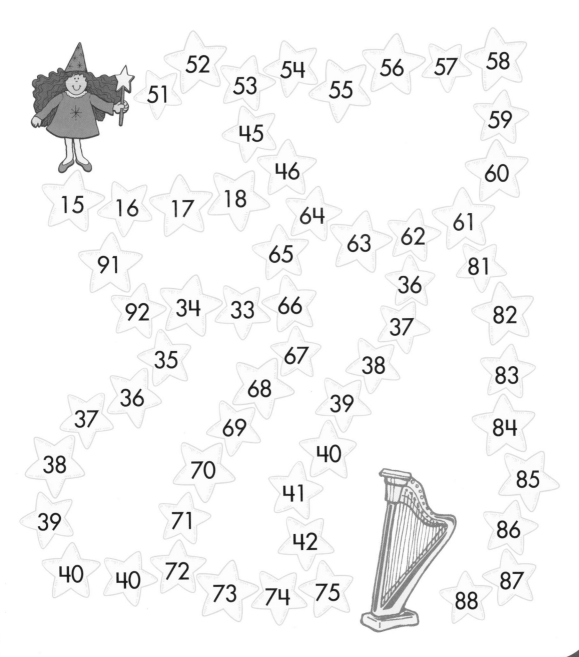

Find the Sandcastle

Circle the numbers **between 40 and 50** to get to the sandcastle.

41   42   43

39   44

19   52

47   46   45

28

13   48   37

56   2   49

Bird's Path to 10

Draw a line along the path of numbers that **add up to 10** to help the bird find the nest.

Start

7	6	2	3	2
3	6	5	4	1
2	3	0	8	9
4	0	1	1	0
3	2	4	9	2

Finish

A Shark's Lunch

Add. Then circle all the fish with **sums of 9 or more** to show which fish the shark ate for lunch.

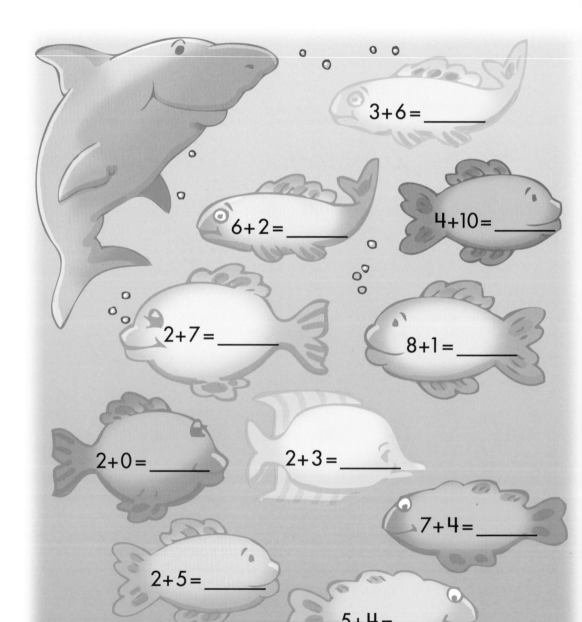

$3+6 =$ _____

$6+2 =$ _____

$4+10 =$ _____

$2+7 =$ _____

$8+1 =$ _____

$2+0 =$ _____

$2+3 =$ _____

$7+4 =$ _____

$2+5 =$ _____

$5+4 =$ _____

Catch the Bus!

Color the squares with **odd numbers** to help Jason catch the school bus.

9	2	14	10	22
23	26	20	30	6
11	5	17	13	19
8	24	34	28	7
18	12	4	16	3

SCHOOL BUS

More Missing Numbers

Write the missing numbers to help the butterfly find the flower garden.

31			34	
	37			40
		43		45
	47	48		
51			54	
			59	60

Place Value Path

Circle the numbers with a **9** in the **tens place** to help the duck find the pond.

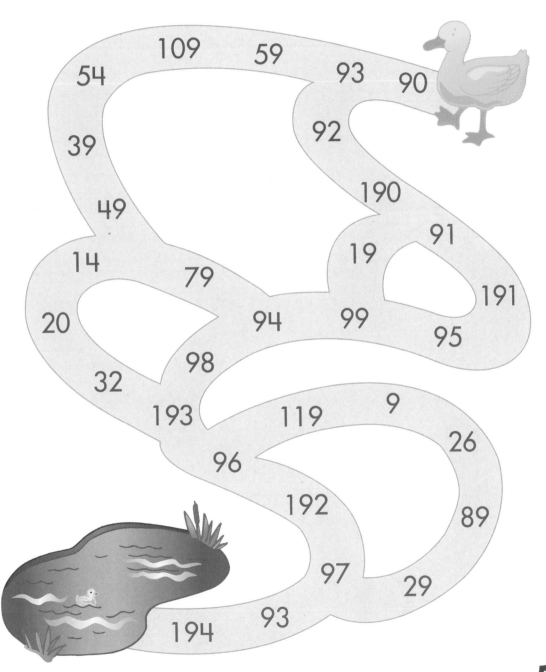

109 59 54 93 90 39 92 49 190 14 79 91 19 20 94 99 191 95 98 32 193 119 9 96 26 192 89 97 29 93 194

Add 5

Add 5 to the number in each igloo and write the answers. Then color the igloo with the largest sum to find the penguin's home.

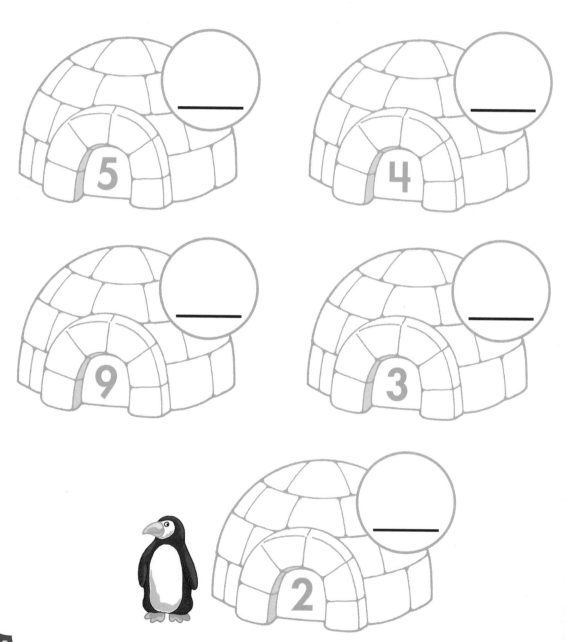

Fire Rescue

Draw a line on the path that goes from **76** to **100** to help the firefighter find the fire truck.

Subtraction Express

Subtract the numbers along the path from the engine to the caboose.

$$\begin{array}{r} 55 \\ -\ 3 \\ \hline \end{array}$$

$$\begin{array}{r} 24 \\ -\ 1 \\ \hline \end{array}$$

$$\begin{array}{r} 48 \\ -\ 4 \\ \hline \end{array}$$

$$\begin{array}{r} 57 \\ -\ 2 \\ \hline \end{array}$$

$$\begin{array}{r} 28 \\ -\ 6 \\ \hline \end{array}$$

$$\begin{array}{r} 99 \\ -\ 7 \\ \hline \end{array}$$

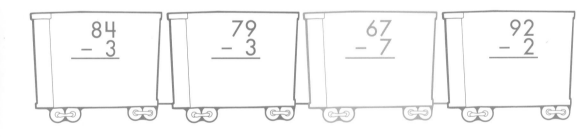

$$\begin{array}{r} 84 \\ -\ 3 \\ \hline \end{array}$$

$$\begin{array}{r} 79 \\ -\ 3 \\ \hline \end{array}$$

$$\begin{array}{r} 67 \\ -\ 7 \\ \hline \end{array}$$

$$\begin{array}{r} 92 \\ -\ 2 \\ \hline \end{array}$$

$$\begin{array}{r} 83 \\ -\ 2 \\ \hline \end{array}$$

$$\begin{array}{r} 99 \\ -\ 4 \\ \hline \end{array}$$

$$\begin{array}{r} 29 \\ -\ 6 \\ \hline \end{array}$$

Hop Home!

Circle the objects along the path that shows a broccoli – carrot pattern to help the rabbit find his home.

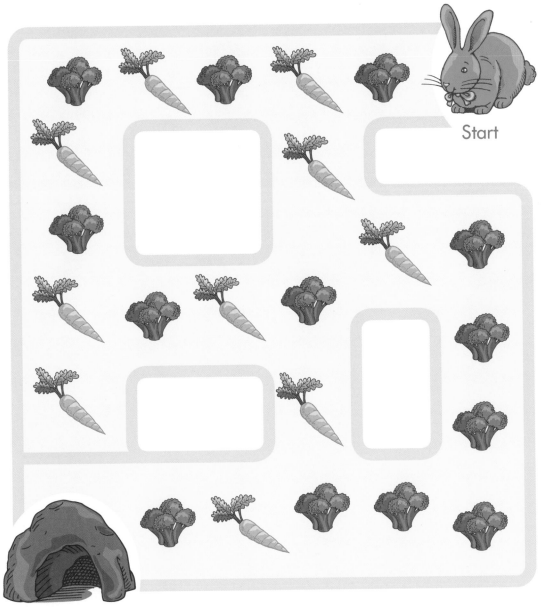

Start

Finish

Make 50¢

Put an **X** in all of the spaces with coins that make
50¢ to help Bill put his money into the piggy bank.

Start

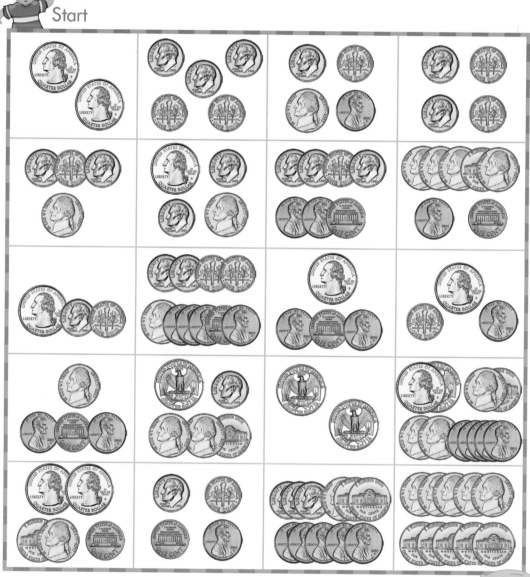

Finish

Add 10

Add 10 to each number. Write the answers on the horses.
Circle the largest sum to find the winner of the race.

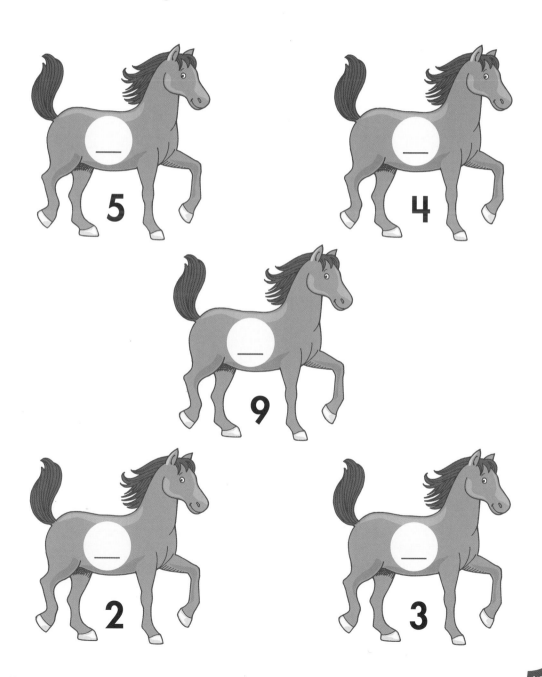

To the Pizza Party

Circle the numbers **between 50 and 60** to help the friends find the pizza party.

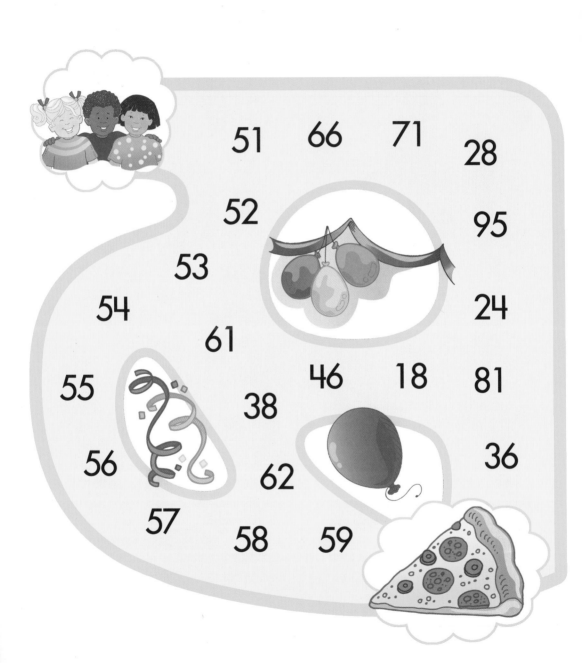

51 66 71 28

52 95

53 24

54

61

55 46 18 81

38

56 36

62

57

58 59

The Pirate's Path

Color the path with numbers that have a **3** in the **tens place** to help the pirate find his treasure chest.

23　25　14

63　0　33

20　43　9　30　93

44　29　131　22

82　71　39

36　28　18　32

133　31　34　130

Apples by Two

Count by **2s** to fill in the apples.

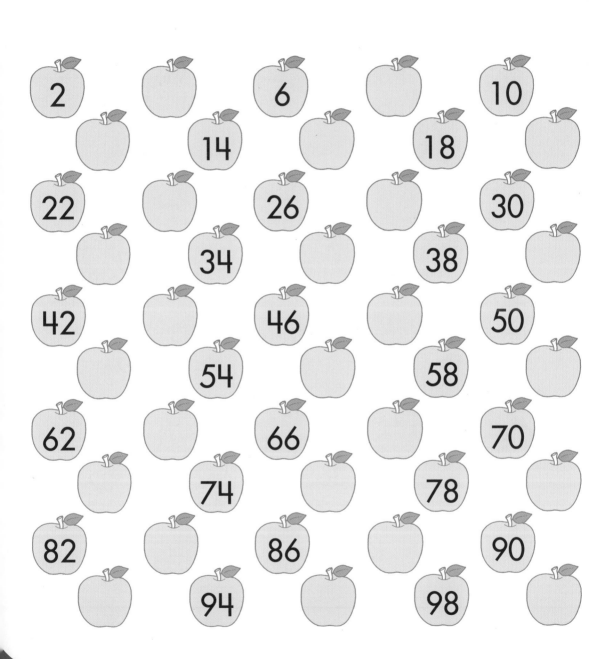

2   6   10

14   18

22   26   30

34   38

42   46   50

54   58

62   66   70

74   78

82   86   90

94   98

Missing Duckling

Subtract. Color the squares with **differences** of **less than 10** to help the mother duck find her missing duckling.

17 − 15	11 − 11	50 − 30	12 − 2
34 − 12	43 − 40	29 − 26	39 − 30
22 − 12	14 − 4	65 − 54	10 − 9
86 − 40	92 − 41	78 − 47	10 − 3

Patty's Piggy Bank

Draw a line along the path of coins with the greatest total value. Then write how much money is in Patty's piggy bank.

The Ladybug Trail

Circle the numbers that have a **6** in the **ones** or **tens place** to help the ladybug find all of her friends.

START

6	29	64	30

54

57	628	61	62

49

16	166	691

100

63	78	60	86	46

96

66	56	633	160

26

FINISH!

106	36	76

Secret Subtraction

Circle **12** more subtraction problems in this puzzle.
Answers can go across or down.

19	20	20	0	19
2	18	6	12	12
17	3	14	7	7
16	15	1	5	4
11	7	4	2	3

A Space Trip

Solve each problem on the path to help the alien get to his planet.

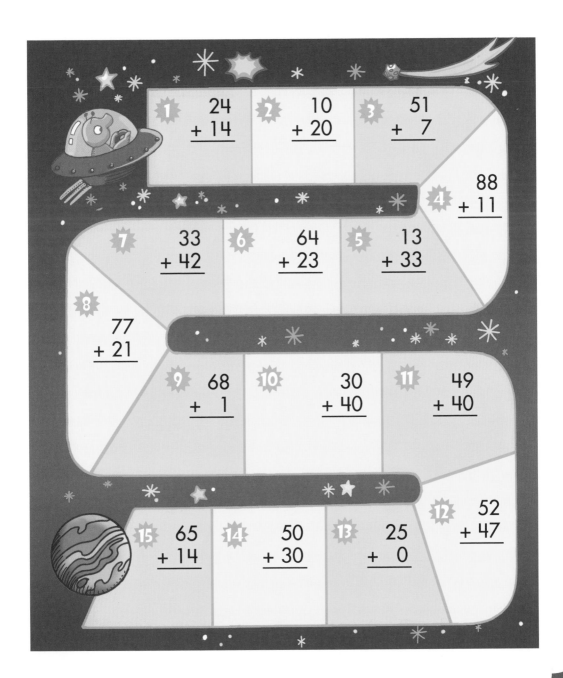

1. 24
    + 14

2. 10
    + 20

3. 51
    + 7

4. 88
    + 11

5. 13
    + 33

6. 64
    + 23

7. 33
    + 42

8. 77
    + 21

9. 68
    + 1

10. 30
    + 40

11. 49
    + 40

12. 52
    + 47

13. 25
    + 0

14. 50
    + 30

15. 65
    + 14

Mother Hen

Draw a line along the path that shows a chick–egg pattern to help the hen find her nest.

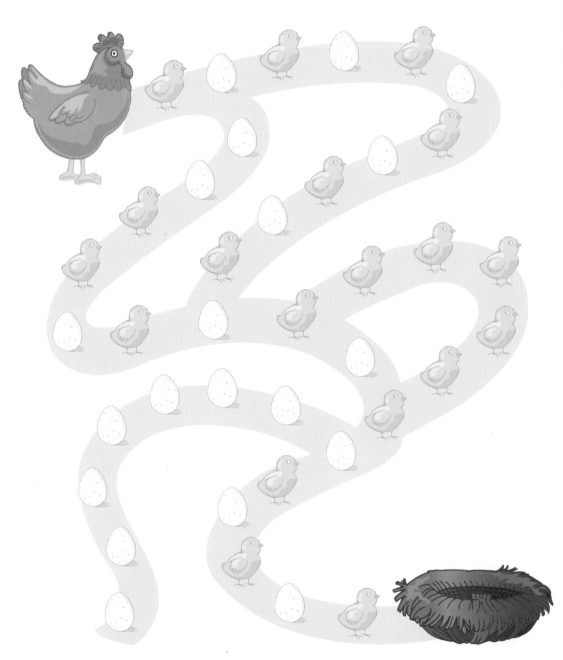

A Bear's Sweet Treat

Add and subtract. Circle the answers that are **less than 10** to help the bear find the honey.

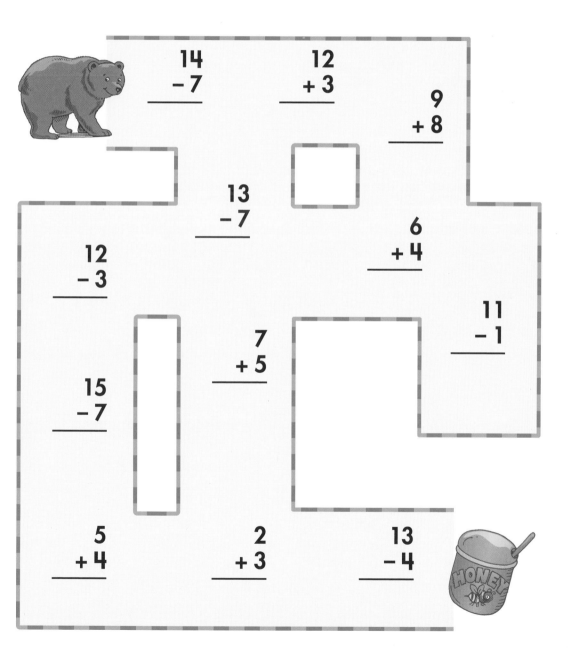

$$14 - 7$$

$$12 + 3$$

$$9 + 8$$

$$13 - 7$$

$$6 + 4$$

$$12 - 3$$

$$11 - 1$$

$$7 + 5$$

$$15 - 7$$

$$5 + 4$$

$$2 + 3$$

$$13 - 4$$

Answer Key

PAGE 2

The Beehive Maze

PAGE 3

Friendship Bracelets

PAGE 4

Find the Doghouse

PAGE 5

Missing Numbers

PAGE 6

Something Fishy

PAGE 7
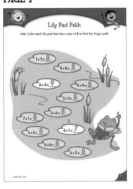
Lily Pad Path

PAGE 8
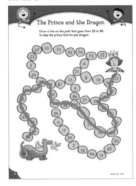
The Prince and the Dragon

PAGE 9
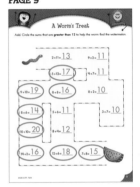
A Worm's Treat

PAGE 10

Beth's Birthday Cake

PAGE 11
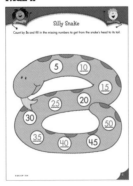
Silly Snake

PAGE 12

Busy Beaver

PAGE 13
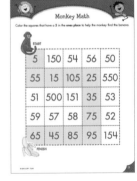
Monkey Math

52

PAGE 14

Watch Out for the Cat!

Count by 5s and fill in the missing numbers to help the mice get to the cheese.

15 20 25 30 35
60 55 50 45 40
65
70 75 80 85 90

PAGE 15

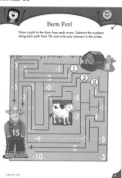

Farm Fun!

Draw a path to the farm from each arrow. Subtract the numbers along each path from 15, and write your answers in the circles.

1 · 3 · 0 · 15

PAGE 16

Counting by Twos

Count by 2s and circle the numbers that lead to the playground.

1 2 3 4 5 6 7 8 9 10 11 12 13 14 15 16 17 18 100

PAGE 17

Soap Box Derby

Circle the numbers that are greater than 50 to help the mouse win the trophy.

START 51 25 42 68 72
17 85 50 49
99 101 82 24 28
67 36 43 91 55 105 13 22 53 32 88
FINISH 78 69 41

PAGE 18

Camel Crossing

Subtract to find the answers. Then color answers in the sand to make a path for the camel.

1) $18 - 3 = 15$
2) $14 - 7 = 7$
3) $10 - 7 = 3$
4) $17 - 6 = 11$
5) $20 - 11 = 9$
6) $16 - 15 = 1$
7) $19 - 14 = 5$

18 5 7 4 10 6
23 3 13 33
16 11 21 24
2 9 6 19
1 39 22 17
15 12 25 8

PAGE 19

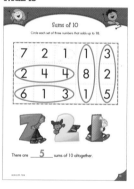

Sums of 10

Circle each set of three numbers that adds up to 10.

7 2 1 1 3
2 4 4 8 2
6 1 3 1 5

There are 5 sums of 10 altogether.

PAGE 20

The Farmer's Veggies

Start with 10. Subtract the numbers between the farmer and each veggie. Write the answers on the veggies.

10
-1 -3 -0
6 -2 7
-3 -1 -2
-1 -2
4 5 4

PAGE 21

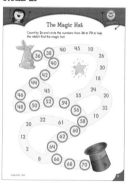

The Magic Hat

Count by 2s and circle the numbers from 36 to 70 to help the rabbit find the magic hat.

36 38 40 45 10 26
40 20
42 18
44 24
46 45 32
48 50 52 54 56 10
20 22 61 58 60
12 62
2 64 66 68 70
8

PAGE 22

Sunflower Addition

Add the numbers along the path from the sun to the sunflower.

$2+7=9$ $26+4=30$ $14+5=19$ $9+0=9$
$1+8=9$ $7+5=12$ $11+3=14$ $10+1=11$
$3+9=12$ $4+4=8$ $12+3=15$ $23+6=29$ $7+7=14$
$31+4=35$ $5+6=11$ $18+2=20$ $9+8=17$

PAGE 23

Number Bubbles

Follow the directions.

1) Start on 1 and count by twos. Fill in the missing numbers.
1 3 5 7 9 11 13 15 17 19

2) Start on 5 and count by fives. Fill in the missing numbers.
5 10 15 20 25 30 35 40 45 50

3) Start on 17 and count by tens. Fill in the missing numbers.
17 27 37 47 57 67 77 87 97 107

4) Start on 100 and count backward by twos. Fill in the missing numbers.
100 90 80 70 60 50 40 30 20 10

5) Start on 85 and count backward by fives. Fill in the missing numbers.
85 80 75 70 65 60 55 50 45 40

PAGE 24

Hop Home

Add. Circle the sums that are less than 10 to help the frog hop home.

START
$5+1=6$ $3+3=6$ $4+7=11$ $5+2=7$
$8+3=11$ $2+3=5$ $6+6=12$ $6+2=8$
$3+8=11$ $2+2=4$ $10+1=11$ $4+4=8$
$3+6=9$ $3+4=7$ $6+6=12$ $6+6$
FINISH

PAGE 25

Picnic Guest

Draw a path to the picnic basket from each arrow. Subtract the numbers along each path from 19. Write your answers in the circles.

2 1 5 19

PAGE 26

Find the Fact Families

Circle the fact families to follow the path and help the girl get home.

9+4=13
4+9=13

11+3=14
7+7=14

5+7=12
7+5=12

6+3=9
7+2=9

8+6=14
6+8=14

12+4=16
10+6=16

5+5=10
7+3=10

9+9=18
10+8=18

4+5=9
8+1=9

12+8=20
8+12=20

9+2=11
5+6=11

3+4=7
4+3=7

13+6=19
6+13=19

PAGE 27

Subtraction Math Path

Start with 20 and subtract the numbers along the path to find the final answer.

Start	20	−		−	1	−
		2	4	2		
		5	−	0	3	= Finish 3

PAGE 28

An Icy Path

Find the sums. Then color answers in the water to make a path for the penguin.

1. 2 + 2 = **4**
2. 10 + 2 = **12**
3. 22 + 2 = **24**
4. 12 + 2 = **14**
5. 36 + 2 = **38**
6. 24 + 2 = **26**
7. 18 + 2 = **20**

PAGE 29

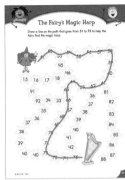

The Fairy's Magic Harp

Draw a line on the path that goes from 51 to 75 to help the fairy find the magic harp.

PAGE 30

Find the Sandcastle

Circle the numbers between 40 and 50 to get to the sandcastle.

41 42 43
39 44
19 52 47 46 45
28 48
13 37
56 2 49

PAGE 31

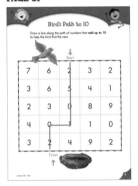

Bird's Path to 10

Draw a line along the path of numbers that add up to 10 to help the bird find the nest.

Start

7	6	2	3	2
3	6	5	4	1
2	3	0	8	9
4	0	1	1	0
3	2	4	9	2

Finish

PAGE 32

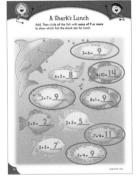

A Shark's Lunch

Add. Then circle all the fish with sums of 9 or more to show which fish the shark ate for lunch.

3+6= 9
6+2= 8
4+10= 14
2+7= 9
8+1= 9
2+0= 2
2+3= 5
7+4= 11
2+5= 7
5+4= 9

PAGE 33

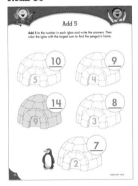

Catch the Bus!

Color the squares with odd numbers to help Jason catch the school bus.

9	2	14	10	22
23	26	20	30	6
11	5	17	13	19
8	24	34	28	7
18	12	4	16	3

PAGE 34

More Missing Numbers

Write the missing numbers to help the butterfly find the flower garden.

31	32	33	34	35
36	37	38	39	40
41	42	43	44	45
46	47	48	49	50
51	52	53	54	55
56	57	58	59	60

PAGE 35

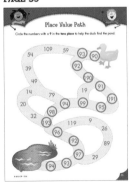

Place Value Path

Circle the numbers with a 9 in the tens place to help the duck find the pond.

54 109 59 93 90
39 92
49 91
14 79 19
20 94 91
32 98
193 119 9 26
92 89
94 93 29

PAGE 36

Add 5

Add 5 to the number in each igloo and write the answers. Then color the igloo with the largest sum to find the penguin's home.

5 → **10**
4 → **9**
9 → **14**
3 → **8**
2 → **7**

PAGE 37

Fire Rescue

Draw a line on the path that goes from 76 to 100 to help the firefighter find the fire truck.

54

Subtraction Express
Subtract the numbers along the path from the engine to the caboose.

55 − 3 = 52	24 − 1 = 23

| 48 − 4 = 44 | 57 − 2 = 55 | 28 − 6 = 22 | 99 − 7 = 92 |

| 84 − 3 = 81 | 79 − 3 = 76 | 67 − 7 = 60 | 92 − 2 = 90 |

| 83 − 2 = 81 | 99 − 4 = 95 | 29 − 6 = 23 |

Hop Home!
Circle the objects along the path that shows a broccoli – carrot pattern to help the rabbit find his home.

Start

Finish

Make 50¢
Put an X on all of the spaces with coins that make 50¢ to help Bill put his money into the piggy bank.

Start

Finish

Add 10
Add 10 to each number. Write the answers on the horses. Circle the largest sum to find the winner of the race.

15 → 5
14 → 4
19 → 9
12 → 2
13 → 3

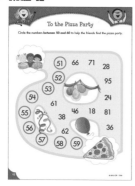

To the Pizza Party
Circle the numbers between 50 and 60 to help the friends find the pizza party.

51 66 71 28
52   95
53   24
54 61
55 38 46 18 81
56   62   36
57 58 59

The Pirate's Path
Color the path with numbers that have a 3 in the tens place to help the pirate find his treasure chest.

23 25 14
63 0 33
20 43 9 30 93
44 29 131 22
82 71 39
36 28 18 32
133 31 34 130

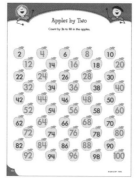

Apples by Two
Count by 2s to fill in the apples.

2 4 6 8 10
12 14 16 18 20
22 24 26 28 30
32 34 36 38 40
42 44 46 48 50
52 54 56 58 60
62 64 66 68 70
72 74 76 78 80
82 84 86 88 90
92 94 96 98 100

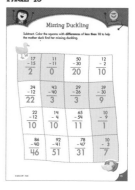

Missing Duckling
Subtract. Color the squares with differences of less than 10 to help the mother duck find her missing duckling.

17 − 15 = 2	11 − 11 = 0	50 − 30 = 20	12 − 2 = 10
34 − 12 = 22	43 − 40 = 3	29 − 26 = 3	39 − 30 = 9
22 − 12 = 10	14 − 4 = 10	65 − 54 = 11	10 − 9 = 1
86 − 40 = 46	92 − 41 = 51	78 − 47 = 31	10 − 3 = 7

Patty's Piggy Bank
Draw a line along the path of coins with the greatest total value. Then write how much money is in Patty's piggy bank.

$1.03

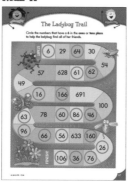

The Ladybug Trail
Circle the numbers that have a 6 in the ones or tens place to help the ladybug find all of her friends.

START
6 29 64
57 628 61 62
54
49
16 166 691
100
63 78 60 86 46
96
66 56 633 160
26
FINISH
106 36 76

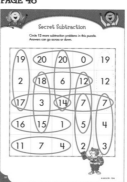

Secret Subtraction
Circle 12 more subtraction problems in this puzzle. Answers can go across or down.

19 20 20 0 19
2 18 6 12 12
17 3 14 7 7
16 15 1 5 4
11 7 4 2 3

A Space Trip
Solve each problem on the path to help the alien get to his planet.

24 + 14 = 38
10 + 20 = 30
51 + 7 = 58
88 + 11 = 99
33 + 42 = 75
64 + 23 = 87
13 + 43 = 56
77 + 21 = 98
68 + 1 = 69
30 + 40 = 70
49 + 40 = 89
65 + 14 = 79
50 + 30 = 80
25 + 0 = 25
52 + 47 = 99

PAGE 50

Mother Hen

Draw a line along the path that shows a chick-egg pattern to help the hen find her nest.

PAGE 51

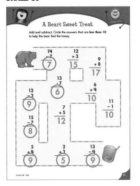

A Bear's Sweet Treat

Add and subtract. Circle the answers that are less than 10 to help the bear find the honey.